Co-Authored by
Taylor Tomu

Co-Authored by
Drew Edwards

Illustrated by
Nandi L. Fernandez

Acknowledgements
Abu Hussein, Alisa Currimjee, Amy Meginnes, Andrew Bauer, Beth Sycamore,
Brandon Wernett, Clay Carnill, Holly Bahn, Isaac Watum, Jessica Bergmann,
Joseph Meginnes, Joseph Mhza, Kevin Oh, Nathan Okiror, Rehmah Kasule,
Robin D'Alessandro

"Neither the World Health Organization nor any other health care provider, agency or
instrumentality of any state or international body has reviewed this text or the recommendations
made herein, and therefore this text does not purport to be recommended or endorsed by any
such organization."

For information regarding permission, write to Pangea Educational Development,
641 W. Lake St. Suite #200, Chicago, IL, USA 60661

ISBN - 978-9970-761-15-9

Published in the Republic of Uganda by Pangea Publishing, a partner of Pangea Educational
Development Group, USA.
Originally published by Pangea Publishing in 2020.

Pangea Publishing is a registered trademark of Pangea Educational Development Group, USA.

Visit us on the web!
www.pangeaeducation.org
www.pangeapublishing.com

Educators and librarians, for a variety of teaching tools, visit us at www.pangeaeducation.org

The Unwelcome Stranger

Pangea
Publishing

About the COVID-19 Pandemic

COVID-19 or the 'Coronavirus' Pandemic began in December of 2019. The virus has quickly spread from country to country, causing danger and spreading fear around the world.

My mom usually picks me up after school everyday on her way home from work. Today Aunt Nikki came to get me. No one told me, but I could tell something was different.

I like Aunt Nikki, she has been living with us while she finishes school and she always has the best games on her phone.

I was trying to play Candy Crush and messages kept messing up the game.
This name "COVID" kept coming up.

"Who is COVID? Is that your new boyfriend?" I asked Auntie Nikki.

"We'll talk about it when we get home," she replied.

Auntie Nikki said we had to go to the store before going home.

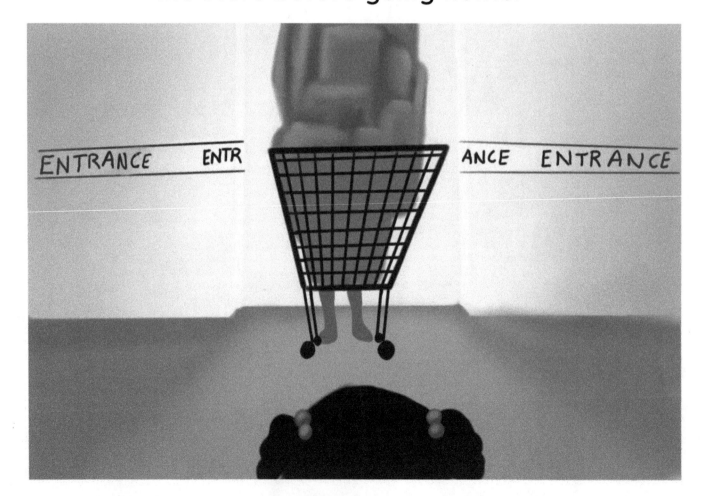

Things were crazy in the store. People were everywhere, grabbing everything, as if they were giving things away for free. I didn't know why, but I could tell something was different.

We walked in to the kitchen and mom was cooking dinner. She turned around and gave me a quick hug.

She grabbed the bags and called Dad to help.

"5 cans of beans, 8 tomatoes, 9 onions, and a loaf of bread," Mom counted. She seemed to be in a hurry.

"We should have enough to last us until my next check," Dad responded. It seemed as if we were preparing for someone to arrive.

"Jazz, take your brother and keep your Granny company until dinner is finished," Mom told me.

We went outside to find Granny working in the garden. It seemed like she was waiting for us.

"Why are all of the adults acting so weird today? Is someone coming over? Is Auntie Nikki getting married?"

"Oh baby, Nikki's not getting married anytime soon. I'm happy you've noticed a change. We need to talk about the Unwelcome Stranger. Come sit by the bug repellant candle—Granny doesn't want to get any mosquito bites."

"Who is the Unwelcome Stranger?"
I nervously asked.

"Not who, but what! It is not a person or an animal, but a virus. The Unwelcome Stranger has been here many times before and will be here many times again. Each time it comes, it disturbs us without warning. It cannot be seen, it cannot be heard, and it brings danger."

"I have been reading a lot of information from the experts at the World Health Organization about its visit this time."

"It behaves like the flu, but it spreads quicker and it makes you sicker. It is impossible to see who does and does not have it."

"Its greatest weapon is causing chaos amongst us," Granny warned. "It is okay to feel fear, but fear does not erase our responsibility to others."

"When we meet fear with knowledge and kindness we can find a way to live cautiously until we defeat the Unwelcome Stranger," Granny said.

"How do we avoid the Unwelcome Stranger?" I asked.

"The best way is to distance ourselves from others by staying home. We will only leave when we have to and we will be careful when we do."

"But we can still see our friends and neighbors, right?" Tyler asked.

"No. For now, we need to stay home with our family. By doing this we protect ourselves and we slow down the Unwelcome Stranger."

"How do we protect ourselves from the Unwelcome Stranger?" I asked.

"We can protect ourselves by washing our hands with soap for at least 20 seconds as often as possible, avoid touching our face and wear a mask if we go outside. All masks should pass the candle test—you shouldn't be able to blow out a candle with it on," Granny responded.

"How do we defeat the Unwelcome Stranger?" Tyler asked.

"The Unwelcome Stranger does not only live within people, but on surfaces for a long time."

"We have to use soaps and bleaches to clean the surfaces that we touch the most," Granny said.

"But what do we do if we become sick?" I asked.

"If you get any symptoms don't panic. You need to tell an adult right way. If you cough or sneeze, you must cover your nose and mouth,"Granny said.

"Things might feel different right now and they will for some time, but if we're careful and work together we can defeat it."

After talking with Granny, we knew exactly what to do. It was time for us to do our part.

We washed our hands and sang the alphabet song twice—I did mine backwards.

We helped with the washing of our busy surfaces.

Most importantly, we have been keeping our distance and reminding others to keep theirs. We even reminded Dad!

We even created a way to help Mom and Dad to safely come home from work everyday.

"Kids, dinner is ready!"
Mother called.

"Look at what an amazing job Jasmine and Tyler did today. If we each do our part and come together as a family and as communities, we will defeat the Unwelcome Stranger," Granny said.

Comprehension Questions

1) What is the Unwelcome Stranger?

2) What do we know about it?

3) What are three things we can do to defeat COVID-19?

4) Once COVID-19 arrives, Jazz notices things changing in her community. Have you noticed changes in your community? What are they?

5) What do you think the characters in the story are feeling? How do you feel?

6) Where does Granny get her information about COVID-19?

Activities

1) Together with your child, walk around the home and identify the busy surfaces that require regular washing.

2) Together with your child, grab a bandana or an old t-shirt and create your own mask by following this link. Don't forget to try the candle test to make sure your mask is safe!

3) List three people you miss. Use any art and craft materials around the house and create a postcard to send them love and support.

4) Create a simple chart to monitor handwashing in the household. As a family, discuss when handwashing should occur:

- Before and after eating
- After using the toilet
- After coming into contact with busy surfaces in the home

Talk Together

BE MINDFUL of your own reactions and your own level of anxiety so that you can model calm.

LISTEN to children and ask what they have heard so you can correct inaccurate information.

RECOGNIZE, validate and empathize with their feelings. Don't try to dismiss or minimize them by telling them not to worry. This does not address their worries.

BE PROACTIVE, don't wait for kids to come to you. Offer to talk and discuss their concerns. This promotes a culture of openness and conversation at home.

Source: Augmented from "How to Talk to Your Kids about the Coronavirus to Ease Their Anxiety" by Dr. Maru Torres-Gregory, PhD, The Family Institute at Northwestern University

Get Accurate Information

COVID-19 is a dangerous virus. Only listen to information from the World Health Organization or your local Ministry of Health on how to prevent, identify, or treat it.

Have questions about COVID-19? We have answers

text hi to

+41 79 781 87 91